Lefse Day

By Heidi Smith & Kari Throop

Illustrated by Heidi Smith

Published by
Nordic Fox Design Co., LLC

For Emilie, our lefse maker
in training.

Special thanks to our Grandmother
and Mother who passed down the
tradition of making lefse.

Farmers grow potatoes
on their farms.

Then they sell their potatoes
to families at the market.

Grandma buys some potatoes at
the market for a special day.

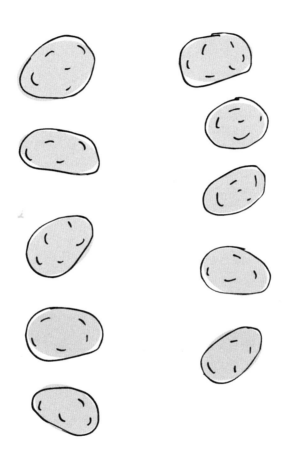

She boils them, mashes them, adds
sugar and salt, then lets them cool
in the fridge overnight.

In the morning, she rices the potatoes and adds butter and flour to make the dough. Now she is ready for the special day.

Today is the special day: it's Lefse Day!
It is a family tradition to make lefse,
a traditional Norwegian flatbread.

It's fun to have the family together
to make lefse because everyone
can be a helper.

Everyone helps form the dough into small balls and then rolls them out into thin flat circles.

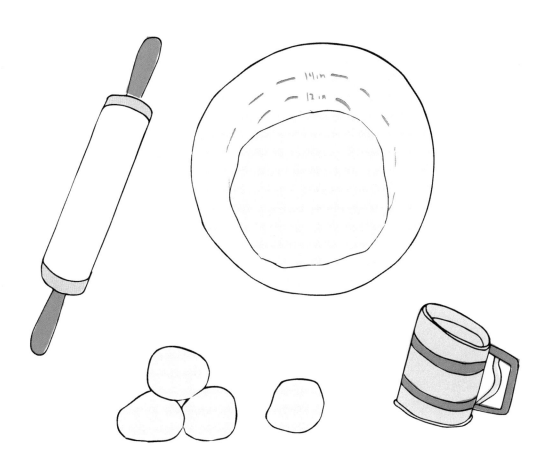

Someone helps move the dough with
a special wooden stick to the griddle,
and turns it to cook on both sides.

Then someone moves the
lefse to the table to cool and
organizes it into piles.

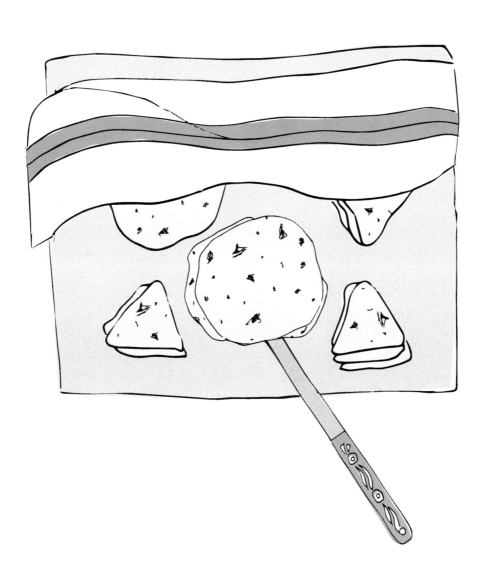

Everyone puts their favorite toppings, like butter, sugar, cinnamon or jam, on the lefse.

Now it's ready to eat.
Everyone is happy when
they eat lefse!

Grandma's Lefse Recipe

6 cups mashed russet potatoes

2 teaspoons salt

1 teaspoon sugar

3 cups flour

1 cup butter

Mix mashed potatoes, sugar and salt. Refrigerate overnight.

Press potatoes through ricer and return to fridge.

Mix flour and butter. Combine mixture with potatoes.

Form into small balls 1.5 inches in diameter. Return balls to fridge.

Roll one ball at a time with covered rolling pin until thin.

Bake dough on both sides on a lefse grill heated to 450 degrees.

Serve rolled with butter, sugar or other toppings.

Enjoy!

Made in the USA
Columbia, SC
05 October 2021